MOON MISSION: Passage to Totality 2017

Our Family's Epic Eclipse Expedition

by Michael Thomas

DORRANCE
PUBLISHING CO
EST. 1920
PITTSBURGH, PENNSYLVANIA 15238

Dorrance Publishing Co
585 Alpha Drive
Pittsburgh, PA 15238
Visit our website at www.dorrancebookstore.com

ISBN: 978-1-4809-5851-7
eISBN: 978-1-4809-5874-6

This book is dedicated with
sympathy to all of the
new Ecliptomaniacs everywhere
who now yearn for their next
Totality "fix" after witnessing the
Great American Total Solar Eclipse
of August 21, 2017.

PREFACE

Astronomy has been a passion of mine since I was twelve when I was given my first telescope. Before that, I was keenly interested in the U.S. Moon Missions and followed each one enthusiastically, especially the Apollo 11 first manned mission to the Moon in 1969.

In a sense, this Eclipse Expedition had become my own "Moon Mission." Not unlike the U.S. Moon Missions, this expedition required much planning, incurred costs, and carried inherent risks, but the outcome proved to be a great success. I am now privileged to share my "Moon Mission."

My first eclipse was in 1970 when I was eleven. I was excited, of course, but viewed from Charlotte, N.C., that eclipse was only 90 percent. And as all Total Solar Eclipse watchers have learned, the difference between a Total Eclipse and a partial eclipse — even if 99.9 percent — is literally like night and day. My first Total Eclipse was in 1991 on the Big Island of Hawaii followed by 1994 on the cruise ship RMS Sagafjord off the coast of Brazil, Aruba in 1998, and then atop the Untersberg near Salzburg in 1999.

I'm not exactly hooked on Eclipse "chasing"; I may go if I want to be where an Eclipse occurs. I'm not going to Siberia, the Sahara, and the Outback, for example.

After an eighteen-year hiatus, I resolved I could not pass up a chance to see my first Total Eclipse on the U.S. Mainland. I planned a trip to St. Maries, Idaho, to visit my sister Terrie, brother-in-law Rich, and nephews Richie, 17, and Jimmy, 14, to coincide with this Eclipse. This was going to be their first Total Eclipse, but they live 267 miles from the path of Totality. We decided to go to Cascade because it is the closest town to the "centerline" with the most services.

That's when I shot for the Moon by renting a travel trailer that was to become our "Lunar Excursion Module." I had zero experience towing an RV, and so I was on a steep learning curve.

My prayers were answered when I was blessed to find the perfect place to park an RV about two weeks beforehand on Craigslist. I even had my pick of the best possible spots on this private estate south of Cascade, Idyllic Small Town U.S.A.

Michael Thomas

Thanks be to the Lord Jesus! We are truly blessed that I am able to find this perfect RVsite by the Payette River when every RV park, campground, hotel, and private home have been fully booked.

The beautiful home of our hostess, Sharon, who has welcomed us onto her estate for our Eclipse Expedition, is nestled on the banks of the Payette River near Cascade. Below reveals its Totality view.

The nearby Trinity Pines Conference Center hosts 350 college students from Northwest Nazarene University in Nampa, Idaho, for "Lights Out in Idaho" Eclipse event. Bottom shows the start of Totality.

The 28 foot Highland Ridge Open Range RV is towed by a Dodge Ram 2500 SLT crew cab 5.7 liter Hemi 4x4 Heavy Duty pickup. This and all aerial images in this book are captured by the Spark quadcopter.

Resolution of the Spark's video camera is high at 1080p and 30fps, and the resolution of its still camera is 12MB. The Spark arrived just in time for this Eclipse. It went on the market in May 2017.

The Spark's first demo Sunday afternoon, August 20, 2017, shows off
its amazing capabilities. Its position is automatically linked to GPS
via its iPhone app which records telemetry for every flight.

Richie's first solo flight is Sunday afternoon, August 20, after we recalibrate the Spark's compass and update its homeport so that the Spark won't try to fly back to Princeville!

I'm smiling because, not only am I hosting Terrie, Rich, Richie, and Jimmy in an amazing place, but now I'm fully digitized unlike my last Eclipse in 1999 when I was still using film and video tape!

Rich is cooking hamburgers on the grill late Sunday after driving six hours along mountainous, hairpinned, and work-laden roads and arriving safely. I arrived Saturday with the RV by the same route.

S'mores on the grill the evening before Eclipse Day is reassurance after everyone arrived safe and sound that we are now fully stoked for the Total Solar Eclipse tomorrow!

Mist rises off the Payette River by our RVsite in the early morning of Eclipse Day, August 21, 2017. "First Contact" occurs at 10:11 a.m. Totality begins at 11:26 a.m. at our location.

Eclipse Day weather is splendid as revealed by this Spark aerial view looking north along the Payette River to Cascade. Any Eclipse Expedition is always undertaken at the vicissitude of the weather.

 Mount Zion Church
August 21

Wait with Me for a while. I have much to tell you. You are walking along the path I have chosen for you. It is both a privileged and a perilous way: experiencing My glorious presence and heralding that reality to others. Sometimes you feel presumptuous to be carrying out such an assignment.

Do not worry about that other people think of you. The work I am doing in you is hidden at first. But eventually blossoms will burst forth, and abundant fruit will be borne. Stay on the path of life with Me. Trust Me wholeheartedly, letting My Spirit fill you with joy and peace.

1 Kings 8:23; Galatians 5:22-23

(from Jesus Calling: Enjoying Peace in His Presence by Sarah Young)

Terrie reads a beautiful devotional whose author specifically wrote it for August 21, 2017, Eclipse Day. These inspirational words remarkably prophesy our own Eclipse Expedition here today to a tee.

Rich gives a beautiful invocation on Eclipse Day, reminding us that
the Great Majesty of our Lord will be gloriously revealed to us today
by signs in the Heavens. Indeed and Amen. Matthew 24:30.

Jimmy is keeping the progressing partial eclipse in view on my Nikon D5600 attached to a 1000mm Celestron C90 mirror lens. All Eclipse images in this book are HD video freeze frames.

15

Jimmy is "eclipsed" by my Mylar solar filter. I have found that no matter which camera I use to record Totality, the images do not fully replicate what my eyes actually see. But I'll keep trying!

As Totality approaches, the temperature drops and daylight takes on a progressively more steely grey hue. Soon, these tree shadows will rapidly disappear as though the Sun were on a "dimmer switch."

"No pressure, Richie, but get the Spark Eclipse video perfect in one take with very little training." Richie delivers like a pro. "The Serene Majesty of the Shadow of the Moon" is now on YouTube.

The partial eclipse lasts 1.25 hours on either side of Totality. The first half becomes progressively more exciting as Totality nears and darkness falls. The second half, well, not so much.

The neophyte "wannabes" wait patiently as the excitement builds. Soon, they will be dragged—willingly, I might add—across the threshold of Totality, to become raving Ecliptomaniacs!

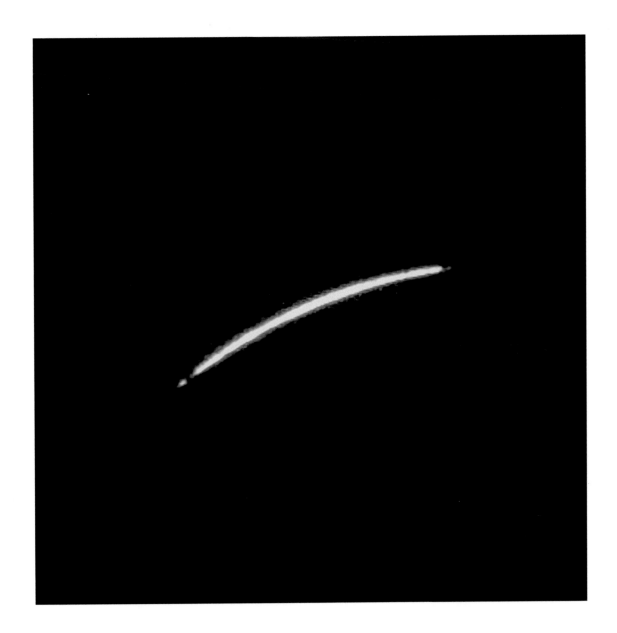

Seconds before totality, Bailey's Beads begin to form by shining
through the craggy lunar limb in the last sliver of sunlight just
before I remove the solar filter from my mirror lens.

At this instant, I remove the solar filter from my 1000mm mirror lens seconds before Totality. I leave the filter off for as long as possible following Totality without damaging my camera's sensor.

At the instant I remove my solar filter, we see an amazing "starburst" of white colored light that most resembles an abstract painting. The Eclipse is not yet safe to view without protective eyewear.

Perhaps the most dramatic event during any Eclipse is the Diamond Ring Effect, heralding Totality. This 4-rayed "Diamond," like a Garnet, resembles the Cross and is clearly a sign in the Heavens.

The Diamond rapidly diminishes before disappearing during Totality
when the Corona blossoms into full view. Astronomers call this
"Second Contact." The Eclipse is now safe to view without eyewear.

Totality is short: only 2 minutes, 2 seconds here just south of
Cascade. A Total Eclipse can last anywhere from 1 second to over 7
minutes. This filtered image reveals layers of fine Coronal detail.

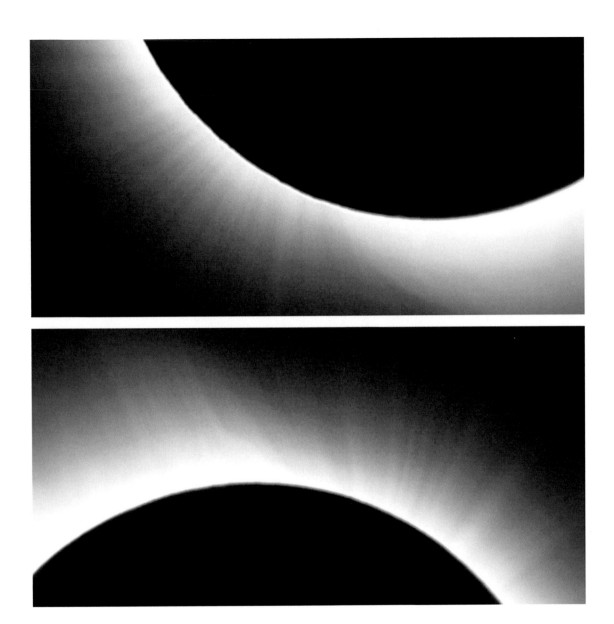

Close-up, split screen HD video freeze frames of Totality reveal the remarkable filamentous detail of the Corona. The fine streamers of plasma follow the Sun's magnetic field lines.

The Diamond Ring Effect marks the end of Totality. Astronomers call this "Third Contact." The dot of light on the upper center of the Moon is a passing satellite captured on video.

The red rim of the Sun's inner atmosphere, or chromosphere, is visible only during a Total Eclipse. The Corona fades away as the Diamond re-emerges, and red solar prominences now become more visible.

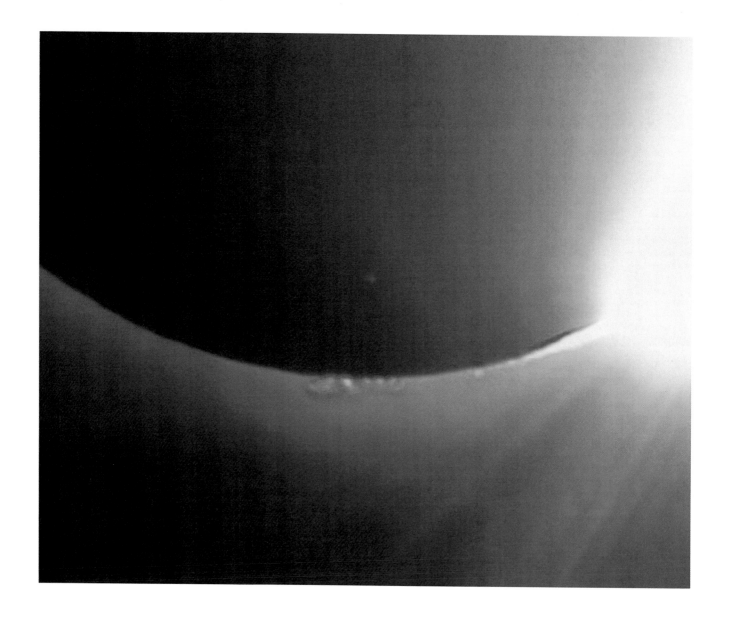

Yet another satellite—more than likely "space junk"—is spotted above
this red solar prominence. Protective eyewear must be worn when
the "surface" of the Sun, or photosphere, blazes back into view.

Exceedingly rare "darkness at noon" on the Payette River at 500ft creates a "360 degree sunset." The next Total Eclipse through Idaho won't occur again for 152 years. Mr. Lincoln never saw an Eclipse!

The Cascade Airport tower beacon, about a mile east of our location, flashes in the sudden darkness of Totality whilst a majestic contrail "comet" passes slowly above. Is this an "Eclipse Flight"?

The Cascade Airport is just as suddenly illuminated less than two minutes later as the Shadow of the Moon can be seen retreating to the east. These Spark video freeze frames were recorded at 500ft.

The contrail "comet" we observed during Totality is revealed to be Southwest Airlines flight 5877 from Spokane to Phoenix after I analyze flight data recorded on Radarbox24.com for August 21, 2017.

Our site is now bathed in the darkness of Totality (above). Nearby, Osprey roost for the "night." Totality may best be viewed with binoculars (enhanced below) or, more simply yet, a pillow!

Totality must be experienced to be understood fully that it is mesmerizing, captivating, transfixing, indeed "addicting." Here the Corona can be seen on the screen of Jimmy's iPad in the darkness.

The Spark's "Osprey's eye view" at 500ft during Totality looks north to Cascade (top) and south toward Smiths Ferry (bottom) whilst the horizon is enveloped in a "360 degree sunset."

After Totality, whilst the Spark is still aloft, I ask Richie to fly the Spark to 700ft where Lake Cascade comes into view to the north and when the Moon's shadow has now retreated to the east.

Kudos to young Richie for his yeoman's effort in skillfully guiding the Spark quadcopter during Totality whilst still having the presence of mind to view the Total Eclipse himself.

Now comes the obligatory, post-Totality Champagne toast to a rewarding "Moon Mission" and a celebration of a First Total Eclipse for the former "wannabe" neophytes, now newly initiated Ecliptomaniacs.

Cheers! The next Total Solar Eclipse now can't come soon enough for these newly committed Ecliptomaniacs. What "medication"—other than Champagne—treats THIS "condition"?

An "extremely seasonal" Eclipse Booth at the American Legion in Cascade purveys a plethora of Ecliptoparaphernalia: eyewear, tee shirts, caps, bags, koozies. Stylish ecliptowear is de rigueur today.

We are sharing an "inside joke" with everyone who has worn "eclipse glasses" and who now knows that we can't see a thing while wearing them, except, of course, for the partially eclipsed Sun.

Post-Eclipse lunch in Cascade is at Whistle Stop Cafe, whose owner, Sharon, is our gracious hostess at our wonderful RVsite. I present Sharon with a nice bottle of wine and chocolate covered macadamia nuts.

We sacrifice 10 more precious seconds of Totality not to travel 18 miles farther south to the "centerline" at Smiths Ferry in order to park here at the perfect site near charming Cascade.

This is the "Bunkhouse" layout of this travel trailer. The two bunks are to the right rear (below), where yours truly and Jimmy slept fitfully the night before the Eclipse, next to all my gear.

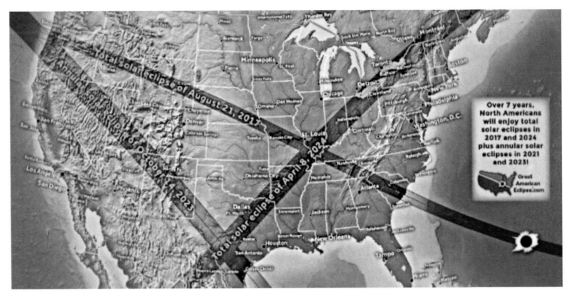

Top map shows Total Eclipse paths of August 21, 2017, and April 8, 2024, and the annular eclipse path of October 14, 2023. Bottom map shows the last transcontinental Total Eclipse path of June 8, 1918.

UBIQUITY

I believe my videography today reveals genuine science regarding the ubiquity of "space junk" in low earth orbit (LEO), the observational prevalence of which heretofore may never have been fully appreciated. A "cloud" of such space debris encircles the Earth and thereby poses an ever increasing risk, not only to operational satellites, but also potentially to safety on the ground.

The "re-entry" of the U.S. discarded space station over the Outback of Australia in 1979 comes to mind. Fortunately, no one was injured by this falling man-made "meteorite," but there is always a next time.

I watched the PBS special on NOVA, "Eclipse Over America," which reveals the exact same phenomenon that I witnessed: Just after Totality, in the glare of the Diamond Ring, focused orbiting objects are perfectly illuminated in the brief time it takes for them to traverse the eclipsed Sun. I captured a half dozen such objects in a few seconds on video freeze frame. NOVA recorded similar objects which did not go unnoticed by me.

MAHALO

Thank you for coming along with us on our Eclipse Expedition to beautiful Cascade, Idaho. We represent every family who experienced the Great American Total Solar Eclipse. But by the Grace of God, we just happened to be in the perfect location and to have the right equipment to be able to record this marvelous event for everyone now to enjoy and to relive for themselves.

I especially wish to thank my seventeen-year-old nephew, Richie, from St. Maries, for his steady hand while guiding the Spark quadcopter under pressure in order to produce a remarkable Eclipse video. Richie's playing of the violin obviously helped!

Aloha from Michael Thomas
in Princeville on Kauai's North Shore, Hawaii

AFTERWORD

A Total Eclipse wields Divine power: It commands not only the influence to compel one, so inclined, to spend thousands of dollars and to travel thousands of miles without any guarantee of witnessing Totality, but also the dominion to thwart totally one's observations. At the instant of Totality, one's best laid viewing plans typically go horribly awry. I have termed this hypnotic state "Ecliptodysphasia," when one's brain becomes so enamored in awe of the experience that it shuts out everything else. This is when one forgets to remove one's solar filter or, indeed, when one forgets one's own name.

Eclipse chasing is thus a double edged sword. On the one hand, one seeks to chase Totality with enthusiasm in order to relive and perhaps fully to capture this extraordinary experience. On the other hand, the quest of actually fully capturing Totality may always exceed one's own grasp. The reality is that Totality can be captured only in the mind's eye and not through any camera lens. That is why one can never fully explain this experience to the uninitiated, and the quest of Totality may itself always be its own reward.